CGP has it all (net)worked out...

GCSE Computer Science exams are pretty tough — but don't worry, this brilliant CGP book is here to RAM home your revision!

It's packed with 10-Minute Tests covering every topic from the new OCR course — including tricky programming skills. Perfect for quick bursts of digestible practice.

And with answers for all questions at the back of the book, it'd be a logic error to choose anyone other than CGP!

CGP — still the best ☺

Our sole aim here at CGP is to produce the highest quality books — carefully written, immaculately presented and dangerously close to being funny.

Then we work our socks off to get them out to you — at the cheapest possible prices.

Published by CGP

Editors:
Liam Dyer, Sammy El-Bahrawy, Michael Weynberg

Contributor:
Oliver Kerr

ISBN: 978 1 78908 559 4

With thanks to Chris Charles and Simon Little for the proofreading.
With thanks to Lottie Edwards for the copyright research.

Printed and bound by Bell & Bain Ltd, Glasgow.

Based on the classic CGP style created by Richard Parsons.

Contents

Section 1: Components of a Computer System

Test 1

There are **12 questions** in this test. Give yourself **10 minutes** to answer them all.

1. Which of these contains instructions used by the CPU when a computer is booting up?

    A   Hard disk drive

    B   RAM

    C   ROM

    [1]

2. Which part of the CPU performs operations such as AND, OR and NOT?

    A   Arithmetic Logic Unit (ALU)

    B   Control Unit (CU)

    C   Memory Data Register (MDR)

    [1]

3. A device driver is a piece of software which...

    A   ... provides a user interface.

    B   ... allows an OS to interact with internal hardware or peripherals.

    C   ... manages user files and applications.

    [1]

4. Which of the following types of storage media are commonly used by businesses to archive large amounts of data?

    A   Hard disk drive

    B   Optical disc

    C   Magnetic tape

    [1]

5. Processor registers temporarily hold small amounts of data needed by...

    A   ... the CPU.

    B   ... RAM.

    C   ... the hard disk drive.

    [1]

6. Which of these types of storage generally has the highest cost per gigabyte?

    A   Solid state drives

    B   Hard disk drives

    C   Magnetic tape

    [1]

7. True or False? "In the Von Neumann architecture, the same memory unit is used for data and instructions."

    A   True

    B   False

    [1]

8. An operating system helps with file management by...

    A   ... compressing every file.

    B   ... arranging the files into a hierarchical structure.

    [1]

9. Give an example of a device which is likely to contain an embedded system.

....

....

[1]

10. How does virtual memory impact a computer's performance?

....

....

[1]

11. Outline how encryption software can help to keep data secure.

....

....

....

....

[2]

12. Explain what happens during the 'fetch' stage of the fetch-execute cycle.

....

....

....

....

....

....

[3]

15

Section 1: Components of a Computer System

Test 2

There are **11 questions** in this test. Give yourself **10 minutes** to answer them all.

1. ROM is...

   A ... volatile.

   B ... non-volatile.

[1]

2. Hard disk drives are a type of...

   A ... primary storage.

   B ... secondary storage.

   C ... tertiary storage.

[1]

3. True or False? "SSDs experience the same fragmentation problems as HDDs."

   A True

   B False

[1]

4. Clock speed is...

   A ... the number of instructions that a CPU can process at the same time.

   B ... the number of cycles per second that a CPU can carry out.

[1]

5. Cache memory has...

   A ... a large capacity that is slow for the CPU to access.

   B ... a large capacity that is quick for the CPU to access.

   C ... a small capacity that is quick for the CPU to access.

[1]

6. RAM is used for...

   A ... storing instructions that tell the CPU how to boot up.

   B ... archiving information.

   C ... storing data, files and programs that are in use.

[1]

7. Virtual memory is used when...

   A ... RAM is full of data.

   B ... the hard drive is full of data.

   C ... ROM is full of data.

[1]

8. What type of utility software scrambles data to stop third-parties from accessing it?

   A Defragmentation

   B Compression

   C Encryption

[1]

---

9. What is the purpose of the CPU?

....

....
[1]

10. What are two main functions of an operating system?

1. ....

....

2. ....

....
[2]

11. Greg is building his own PC and is deciding whether to have
a Hard Disk Drive (HDD) or a Solid State Drive (SSD).
Give two advantages and two disadvantages of choosing the SSD instead of the HDD.

Advantages:

1. ....

....

2. ....

....

Disadvantages:

1. ....

....

2. ....

....
[4]

15

Test 3

There are **12 questions** in this test. Give yourself **10 minutes** to answer them all.

1. Which type of user interface requires the most resources to run?

   A Command line interface

   B Graphical user interface

   [1]

2. Embedded systems are designed to...

   A ... carry out a single task efficiently.

   B ... carry out a variety of tasks.

   [1]

3. An OS may make use of a buffer when transferring data. Buffers are used...

   A ... for temporary data storage.

   B ... for long-term data storage.

   [1]

4. Which type of storage generally has the fastest read/write speed?

   A Memory card

   B Optical disc

   C Solid state drive

   [1]

5. True or False? "The OS gives some processes a higher priority for execution by the CPU than others."

   A True

   B False

   [1]

6. Increasing the number of cores in a CPU...

   A ... increases the number of instructions processed by each core per second.

   B ... increases the number of instructions that can be carried out at the same time.

   [1]

7. Which of the following is an example of a magnetic storage device?

   A Memory card

   B DVD

   C HDD

   [1]

8. Which of the following components controls the flow of data in the CPU?

   A ALU

   B OS

   C CU

   [1]

9. Sian uses compression software on a file. Give one benefit of compressing the file.

....

....

[1]

10. What is the function of the accumulator?

....

....

[1]

11. Give two security measures an OS may have to prevent unauthorised access.

1. ....

2. ....

[2]

12. A teacher wants to provide each of their students with some files and open-source software, which will take up 6.5 GB of storage space.

State an appropriate storage device to use. Give two reasons for your answer.

Storage device: ....

1. ....

....

2. ....

....

[3]

15

Test 4

There are **11 questions** in this test. Give yourself **10 minutes** to answer them all.

1. Which of these units of data is the largest?

    A   Gigabyte

    B   Megabyte

    C   Terabyte

    [1]

2. Which of the following denary values represents the hexadecimal character "E"?

    A   15

    B   13

    C   14

    [1]

3. Unicode® is a character set which has characters for...

    A   ... all major languages.

    B   ... the English language only.

    [1]

4. The size of a sound file (in bits) is calculated using the formula...

    A   ... sample rate × bit depth + duration

    B   ... sample rate × bit depth × duration

    C   ... sample rate ÷ bit depth + duration

    [1]

5. Which of the following binary numbers represents the denary value 33?

    A   00100001

    B   01000001

    C   00010001

    [1]

6. The most significant bit of an 8-bit binary number is...

    A   ... the left-most bit.

    B   ... the right-most bit.

    [1]

7. How many characters are in the ASCII character set?

    A   64

    B   128

    C   256

    [1]

8. Pixels are...

    A   ... small dots that make up a bitmap image.

    B   ... pieces of information that contain an image's file format, colour depth, etc.

    [1]

9. Add the binary numbers 01010101 and 01101101.

[2]

10. Explain what is meant by 'overflow'.

....

....

....

....

[2]

11. A photographer wants to compress some high-quality images so they can be stored on an external hard drive, while maintaining the quality of the images.

Which type of compression should the photographer use?

....

[1]

Explain why this type of compression is the most appropriate for the photographer.

....

....

....

....

[2]

15

Test 5

There are **11 questions** in this test. Give yourself **10 minutes** to answer them all.

1. A one place left shift on a binary number...

   A   ... doubles the number.

   B   ... halves the number.

   [1]

2. All data must be converted into...

   A   ... a binary format to be processed by a computer.

   B   ... a hexadecimal format to be processed by a computer.

   [1]

3. How many bits are in a kilobyte?

   A   8000

   B   1000

   C   4

   [1]

4. True or False? "An image's creation date, time and location are all types of metadata."

   A   True

   B   False

   [1]

5. Which of these hexadecimal numbers is the largest?

   A   23

   B   1F

   C   2A

   [1]

6. The process of converting an analogue signal to a digital signal is known as...

   A   ... compression.

   B   ... re-coding.

   C   ... sampling.

   [1]

7. Hexadecimal numbers are often used by programmers instead of binary numbers because...

   A   ... there are fewer hexadecimal numbers than binary numbers.

   B   ... they are shorter, which makes them easier to remember.

   [1]

8. Increasing the number of bits used for each pixel in an image will...

   A   ... increase the range of colours that the image can display.

   B   ... decrease the resolution of the image.

   C   ... have no effect on the file size.

   [1]

9. Ben opens a text file. It contains 30 characters, as shown below.
   Each character is represented using the ASCII character set.

   > Calzones? Yes, they are yummy!

   The binary representation for the character 'y' is 01111001.
   What is the binary representation for the character 'z'?

   ....
   [1]

   Calculate the size of the text file in bits.

   ....

   ....
   [2]

10. Convert the hexadecimal number 5E into binary.

    ....

    ....

    ....
    [2]

11. A singer is recording the vocal tracks for their new album.
    A sound engineer increases the sample rate and bit depth of the recordings.
    Outline one benefit and one drawback of these changes.

    Benefit: ....

    ....

    Drawback: ....

    ....
    [2]

    15

Test 6

There are **11 questions** in this test. Give yourself **10 minutes** to answer them all.

1. How many bits are in a nibble?

   A 2

   B 4

   C 8

   [1]

2. A hexadecimal digit can represent...

   A ... 2 different values.

   B ... 10 different values.

   C ... 16 different values.

   [1]

3. What is 00100111 as a denary number?

   A 43

   B 39

   C 78

   [1]

4. Decreasing the sample rate...

   A ... reduces the size of a sound file.

   B ... reduces the bit depth.

   C ... reduces both the size of a sound file and the bit depth.

   [1]

5. Which of the following character sets represents more characters?

   A ASCII

   B Unicode®

   [1]

6. An image file has a size of 4 MB. How much storage space would 1000 copies of this file take up?

   A 4 gigabytes

   B 4 petabytes

   C 40 000 bytes

   [1]

7. Which of the following denary values is equal to the hex value FF?

   A 15

   B 128

   C 255

   [1]

8. The 8-bit binary number 10011001 is added to itself. The calculation would...

   A ... cause an overflow error.

   B ... not cause an overflow error.

   [1]

9. The function shiftR takes an 8-bit binary number, performs a 4 place right shift and returns an 8-bit answer. State what the following would return:

shiftR(00110000) ....

shiftR(11011001) ....

[2]

The function shiftR is used to divide numbers by 16.
Outline why shiftR(11011001) returns an answer with a loss of accuracy.

....

....

[1]

10. Claire has received a compressed version of a file in an email.
Why has compression been used on this file?

....

....

....

....

[2]

11. A program receives the 7-digit binary number 1001000 as an input.
1 is appended to the end of the number and its denary value is output.
What is the output of the program?

....

....

....

[2]

15

Section 2: Data Representation

Section 3: Networks

Test 7

There are **11 questions** in this test. Give yourself **10 minutes** to answer them all.

1. The World Wide Web is based on...

    A ... a client-server relationship.

    B ... a peer-to-peer relationship.

    [1]

2. True or False? "A WAN connects LANs across large geographical distances."

    A True

    B False

    [1]

3. A packet is...

    A ... a type of file.

    B ... a chunk of data being transmitted over a network.

    C ... a network protocol.

    [1]

4. Which of these pieces of hardware transmits data between networks?

    A NIC

    B Switch

    C Router

    [1]

5. What is an advantage of creating a piece of hardware that follows certain standards?

    A It will be compatible with other pieces of hardware.

    B It is much cheaper to manufacture.

    [1]

6. Which type of wireless technology typically has a larger connection range?

    A Wi-Fi®

    B Bluetooth®

    [1]

7. Which of these protocols would be used to upload a large number of files to a remote server?

    A HTTP

    B IMAP

    C FTP

    [1]

8. Which of these is an example of a phishing attack?

    A Downloading software containing a virus from the Internet.

    B Attempting to gain sensitive information by impersonating a trustworthy person or business.

    C Attempting to overload a server to cause it to crash.

    [1]

9. What is the name of the network topology represented in the diagram on the right?

....
[1]

10. Cameron uses a weak password on his computer and has not updated his anti-malware software. How could each of his actions put his computer at risk?

....

....

....

....
[2]

11. Give two advantages and two disadvantages of storing data in the cloud.

Advantages:

1. ....

....

2. ....

....

Disadvantages:

1. ....

....

2. ....

....
[4]

15

Test 8

There are **11 questions** in this test. Give yourself **10 minutes** to answer them all.

1. Which type of cable is best for transmitting data over very large distances without losing signal quality?

    A Coaxial

    B Ethernet

    C Fibre optic

    [1]

2. Which of the following examines data entering and leaving a network in order to block any potential threats?

    A Router

    B Firewall

    C Switch

    [1]

3. Bandwidth is...

    A ... the amount of data that can be transferred in a given time.

    B ... the maximum range of a wireless LAN.

    [1]

4. True or False? "IP addresses are assigned to network-enabled devices by the manufacturer."

    A True

    B False

    [1]

5. A DNS...

    A ... assigns a MAC address to each computer on a network.

    B ... stores domain names and their corresponding IP addresses.

    C ... is used to create a LAN.

    [1]

6. An active attack is when someone...

    A ... in an organisation exploits their network access for malicious purposes.

    B ... monitors and intercepts sensitive data being transferred on a network.

    C ... installs malware on a network with the intent to harm devices.

    [1]

7. Which protocol is responsible for directing data packets between networks?

    A Internet Protocol (IP)

    B File Transfer Protocol (FTP)

    C Hyper Text Transfer Protocol (HTTP)

    [1]

8. IMAP is used for...

    A ... accessing websites.

    B ... retrieving emails.

    C ... moving and editing files.

    [1]

9. Suggest one physical security measure that can help to protect a network.

   ....

   ....
   [1]

10. What are two features of a strong password?

   1. ....

   2. ....
   [2]

11. Two companies are deciding which network model would suit their offices.

Company A	Company B
200 employees Many IT specialists	5 employees No IT specialists

   Suggest why a client-server network may be appropriate for Company A.

   ....

   ....

   ....

   ....

   Suggest why a peer-to-peer network may be appropriate for Company B.

   ....

   ....

   ....

   ....
   [4]

15

Test 9

There are **12 questions** in this test. Give yourself **10 minutes** to answer them all.

1. A MAC address...

   A ... is assigned to a device when it first accesses a network.

   B ... is required for communication between devices on the same network.

   [1]

2. Which of these is likely to have a more stable connection?

   A A wired LAN using Ethernet cables.

   B A wireless LAN using Wi-Fi®.

   [1]

3. What type of attack exploits weak input validation on a website?

   A Phishing

   B SQL injection

   C Denial of service

   [1]

4. POP3 is a protocol which is used to...

   A ... check a packet has arrived at its destination.

   B ... access files across a network.

   C ... retrieve emails from a server.

   [1]

5. A switch is used to....

   A ... transmit data between networks.

   B ... scan data for potential threats.

   C ... connect devices on a LAN.

   [1]

6. Which security measure is the best defence against a passive attack?

   A Data encryption

   B User access levels

   C Anti-malware software

   [1]

7. Which of the following statements about layers of network protocols is true?

   A They discourage developers from creating universal software.

   B They break network communication down into manageable chunks.

   [1]

8. A problem with a wired full-mesh network is that...

   A ... the whole network is affected if a single device has an issue.

   B ... there are lots of data collisions.

   C ... the more devices you add, the more expensive it gets to connect them all.

   [1]

9. Name the protocol that sends encrypted data between a web server and a web browser.

....

....
[1]

10. Give two benefits of using a cloud-based application rather than the same application installed on a local device.

1. ....

....

2. ....

....
[2]

11. A company network may enforce user access levels. What are user access levels?

....

....
[1]

12. Give three reasons why a business may choose to use a LAN instead of using a number of stand-alone (unconnected) devices.

1. ....

....

2. ....

....

3. ....

....
[3]

15

Test 10

There are **12 questions** in this test. Give yourself **10 minutes** to answer them all.

1. True or False? "Peer-to-peer networks do not have a central server."

   A   True

   B   False

   [1]

2. The Internet is an example of a...

   A   ... LAN.

   B   ... WAN.

   [1]

3. File hosting is when...

   A   ... a business uses their servers to store the files of an individual or another business.

   B   ... multiple users access a file at the same time.

   [1]

4. A NIC is a piece of hardware that...

   A   ... allows a device to connect to a network.

   B   ... connects devices on a LAN.

   C   ... transmits data between networks.

   [1]

5. The rules that govern how devices communicate and transmit data across a network are called...

   A   ... protocols.

   B   ... topologies.

   C   ... addresses.

   [1]

6. Penetration testing is...

   A   ... investigating the cause of an attack on a network.

   B   ... detecting malware hidden within files downloaded from the Internet.

   C   ... identifying weaknesses in a network through simulated attacks.

   [1]

7. Which one of these types of malware self-replicates?

   A   Worms

   B   Trojans

   C   Viruses

   [1]

8. The TCP protocol...

   A   ... splits data into packets.

   B   ... encrypts information that is sent and received.

   C   ... is used to send emails.

   [1]

9. What is a denial of service attack?

....

....

[1]

10. A company follows the procedures on the
right to protect the security of their network.
Give two further procedures which could protect them.

> **All employees must:**
>
> - Use strong passwords
>
> - Regularly update
>   anti-malware software

1. ....

....

2. ....

....

[2]

11. Outline the differences between IPv4 and IPv6 addresses.

....

....

....

[2]

12. Give two factors that can impact the performance of a wireless home network.

1. ....

....

2. ....

....

[2]

15

Section 4: Issues

Test 11

There are **12 questions** in this test. Give yourself **10 minutes** to answer them all.

1. Internet censorship is...

   A ... monitoring the websites that a user accesses on the Internet.

   B ... controlling what others can access and publish on the Internet.

   [1]

2. True or False? "The Data Protection Act only applies to organisations who store data on their employees."

   A True

   B False

   [1]

3. Can a company use a copyrighted photo, owned by someone else, on their website?

   A Yes, at any time.

   B Yes, with the owner's permission.

   C No, never.

   [1]

4. Large amounts of E-waste is created as a result of people...

   A ... frequently upgrading to the latest electronic devices.

   B ... putting electronic devices into a sleep or hibernation mode.

   [1]

5. Which of these is a valid reason for a company not to release any data they hold on a person under the Data Protection Act?

   A The company director refuses.

   B The data could affect a court case.

   C The data could damage the business.

   [1]

6. A new online banking app could increase the profits of a bank. Who would be affected by the release of the app?

   A The customers of the bank.

   B The owners of the bank.

   C The customers and owners of the bank.

   [1]

7. A person gains unauthorised access to a computer to steal data. This violates the...

   A ... Data Protection Act.

   B ... Computer Misuse Act.

   C ... Copyright, Designs and Patents Act.

   [1]

8. Proprietary software ...

   A ... is usually paid for.

   B ... can be adapted by users as they need.

   C ... does not get regular updates.

   [1]

9. Suggest a legal or ethical issue that is caused by cloud computing.

....

....

[1]

10. What is meant by the term 'cyberbullying'?

....

....

[1]

11. Give two ways that manufacturing a computer can negatively impact the environment.

1. ....

....

2. ....

....

[2]

12. A supermarket collects contact details from a customer to notify them of future offers.
The data is stored on an unsecure server before being sold to a company, without
the customer's permission, who uses the data to make unrelated sales calls.

Explain how this violates the Data Protection Act.

....

....

....

....

[3]

15

Test 12

There are **11 questions** in this test. Give yourself **10 minutes** to answer them all.

1. Intellectual property is...

   A ... an original idea or piece of work that someone has created and belongs to them.

   B ... a type of legislation which protects copyrighted material.

[1]

2. What type of software allows anyone to legally make modifications to its source code?

   A Open source

   B Proprietary

[1]

3. A cultural issue created by the Internet is that...

   A ... people can communicate more easily over large distances.

   B ... face-to-face social interactions can be neglected.

[1]

4. In accordance with the Data Protection Act, how long should data be kept for?

   A Up to 25 years.

   B Only for as long as it is necessary.

   C There is no limit.

[1]

5. Why might a government restrict access to certain websites?

   A To protect vulnerable members of the public, such as children.

   B To more easily collect data about website browsing habits.

[1]

6. True or False? "Most organisations need to register with the government before they can begin collecting data."

   A True

   B False

[1]

7. Devices consume large amounts of electricity. This has a negative effect on the environment because...

   A ... the majority of electricity is made from non-renewable energy resources.

   B ... producing electricity decreases the amount of pollution in the atmosphere.

[1]

8. Which of the following is likely to consume the most energy?

   A A desktop computer on standby.

   B A smartphone charging.

   C A web server receiving a large amount of client requests.

[1]

9. What is meant by computer surveillance?

....

....
[1]

10. Gareth lives in rural Wales and earns a low income.
Why might he have limited access to technology?

....

....

....
[2]

What is the name given to the inequality created by people
having different levels of access to technology?

....
[1]

11. Give three examples of how technology can have
a negative effect on a teenager's wellbeing.

1. ....

....

2. ....

....

3. ....

....
[3]

15

Test 13

There are **12 questions** in this test. Give yourself **10 minutes** to answer them all.

1. In order to halve a binary number, all bits are...

   A ... shifted 1 place to the left.

   B ... shifted 1 place to the right.

   C ... shifted 2 places to the right.

   [1]

2. True or False? "The purpose of systems software is to run and maintain a computer system."

   A True

   B False

   [1]

3. Which of the following generally has the lowest average capacity?

   A SSD

   B Memory card

   C CD-ROM

   [1]

4. Which part of the CPU holds the memory address for the next instruction to be processed?

   A Memory Address Register (MAR)

   B Accumulator

   C Program Counter (PC)

   [1]

5. The bit depth of an audio file is the number of bits...

   A ... available for each sample.

   B ... processed per second.

   [1]

6. Which of the following types of malware disguises itself as legitimate software?

   A Trojan

   B Worm

   C Virus

   [1]

7. In which of the following scenarios would using cloud storage be most appropriate?

   A A government organisation storing sensitive personal details.

   B A small photography company with photographers working remotely.

   C An author who has limited access to the Internet.

   [1]

8. SMTP is used to...

   A ... retrieve emails from a server.

   B ... send emails and transfer them between servers.

   C ... access websites and communicate with web servers.

   [1]

9. What is a disadvantage of increasing the resolution of an image?

....

....

[1]

10. Give two reasons why a star topology is often used on a LAN.

1. ....

....

2. ....

....

[2]

11. A virtual server is a software-based server. It is possible to run multiple
virtual servers on one physical server. Explain the environmental impact of
using virtual servers on a network instead of multiple physical servers.

....

....

....

....

[2]

12. Describe how a hard disk becomes fragmented.

....

....

....

[2]

15

Test 14

There are **12 questions** in this test. Give yourself **10 minutes** to answer them all.

1. How many unique colours can a 4-bit image use?

   A 8

   B 16

   C 24

   [1]

2. Which of the following does an OS use to communicate with hardware?

   A Device driver software

   B Defragmentation software

   C Graphical user interfaces

   [1]

3. Which CPU would you expect to have the greatest performance? A CPU with...

   A ... 4 cores and 1.5 GHz clock speed.

   B ... 2 cores and 3 GHz clock speed.

   C ... 4 cores and 3 GHz clock speed.

   [1]

4. Which of these is not a Data Protection Act principle?

   A Data should be kept safe and secure.

   B Data must be accurate and up to date.

   C Data cannot be disclosed to anybody.

   [1]

5. Which of the following data amounts is the largest?

   A 400 MB

   B 0.3 GB

   C 8000 KB

   [1]

6. True or False? "Privacy agreements can legally allow companies to target adverts at you using your personal information."

   A True

   B False

   [1]

7. If a website has weak input validation, an SQL injection could...

   A ... reveal sensitive information from a database.

   B ... upgrade the database software version.

   [1]

8. A hacker uses a packet sniffer to intercept and log traffic on a network. Which type of attack is this?

   A Brute force

   B Active

   C Passive

   [1]

9. A restaurant introduces a smartphone app that customers can use to place food orders. Suggest how this decision may affect the waiters of the restaurant.

....

....

[1]

10. Describe how an OS manages memory and the CPU to run multiple applications at the same time.

....

....

....

....

[2]

11. Convert the denary number 142 into hexadecimal.

....

....

....

[2]

12. Tilly's computer is running slowly. Explain how upgrading the RAM could help to improve her computer's performance.

....

....

....

[2]

15

Test 15

There are **12 questions** in this test. Give yourself **10 minutes** to answer them all.

1. FTP is an example of a network protocol. What does FTP stand for?

A Firmware Technology Protocol

B File Transfer Protocol

C Full Topology Protocol

[1]

2. Which of the following correctly calculates the size of a bitmap image file?

A 2^n (where n is the colour depth)

B image height + image width

C colour depth × image height × image width

[1]

3. Which type of task is not handled by a computer's operating system?

A Providing a user interface.

B Managing user accounts.

C Updating all open source software.

[1]

4. Which of the following statements about external hard disk drives is true?

A They have no moving parts.

B They are portable.

C They are unreliable.

[1]

5. True or False? "A company is likely to own all of its WAN infrastructure."

A True

B False

[1]

6. Which device initiates communication in a client-server network?

A Client

B Server

[1]

7. An audio file needs to be compressed. Which of these formats would give a higher quality audio file?

A MP3 (a lossy format)

B FLAC (a lossless format)

[1]

8. Which type of utility software may increase system performance after use?

A Defragmentation software

B Encryption software

[1]

---

9. What is a WAP used for?

....

....

[1]

10. Convert the binary number 10101110 into hexadecimal.

....

....

....

[2]

11. Give two criminal offences which were introduced with the Computer Misuse Act.

1. ....

....

2. ....

....

[2]

12. Suggest two features of a password authentication system which could help to reduce the risk of brute force attacks.

1. ....

....

2. ....

....

[2]

15

Test 16

There are **11 questions** in this test. Give yourself **10 minutes** to answer them all.

1. Blu-ray™ discs can hold around...

    A   ... 250 MB of data.

    B   ... 2.5 GB of data.

    C   ... 25 GB of data.

    [1]

2. In a mesh network, all devices...

    A   ... are connected to a single, centralised switch or server.

    B   ... are connected to each other.

    [1]

3. Which of the following network protocols is used to retrieve an email that is held on a server?

    A   HTTP

    B   SMTP

    C   POP3

    [1]

4. Malware that monitors and sends a user's actions to a hacker is called...

    A   ... spyware.

    B   ... scareware.

    C   ... rootkit.

    [1]

5. What is the largest denary value that can be represented with one hexadecimal digit?

    A   10

    B   16

    C   15

    [1]

6. Which of the following protects new inventions, ideas and concepts, such as a new router design, from being duplicated?

    A   Copyright

    B   Software licences

    C   Patents

    [1]

7. A collection of characters that a computer recognises from their binary representation is called a...

    A   ... font.

    B   ... character set.

    [1]

8. How many applications can be processed by a single core CPU at the same time?

    A   One

    B   Ten

    C   Unlimited

    [1]

9. Complete a 2 place left shift on the 8-bit binary number 00110010.

....

[1]

10. Sort the following types of storage into the table below.

Magnetic Hard Disk, RAM, ROM, SSD, Magnetic Tape, Cache

Primary Storage	Secondary Storage

[2]

11. A company wants to develop an application to manage customer accounts.
Give two positives and two negatives of using an existing piece
of open source software as a starting point for their application.

Positives:

1. ....

....

2. ....

....

Negatives:

1. ....

....

2. ....

....

[4]

15

Test 17

There are **12 questions** in this test. Give yourself **10 minutes** to answer them all.

1. A developer wants to compress some software to send to a client. Which type of compression cannot be used?

   A Lossy

   B Lossless

   [1]

2. The main memory of a computer is its...

   A ... RAM.

   B ... internal hard drive.

   C ... virtual memory.

   [1]

3. What is the denary value of the binary number 00100011?

   A 19

   B 35

   C 36

   [1]

4. Which of the following is equal to 1 petabyte?

   A 1000 terabytes

   B 1000 gigabytes

   C 1000 bytes

   [1]

5. Network protocols operate on different layers. These layers...

   A ... overlap each other.

   B ... are independent of each other.

   [1]

6. Which type of memory is the fastest for the CPU to access?

   A Cache

   B Registers

   C RAM

   [1]

7. Which type of attack stops users accessing a website by flooding the network with large amounts of useless traffic?

   A Denial of service

   B Brute force

   C SQL injection

   [1]

8. Which of the following is usually the weakest point in a computer network?

   A Anti-virus software

   B The users of the system

   C Physical security (padlocks, CCTV, locked doors, etc.)

   [1]

---

9. Why is secondary storage not affected during a power cut?

....

....
[1]

10. Convert the hexadecimal number 4F into denary.

....

....

....
[2]

11. Suggest two ways to reduce the risk of health problems when using a computer.

1. ....

....

2. ....

....
[2]

12. Give one benefit and one drawback of a wired LAN over a wireless LAN.

Benefit: ....

....

Drawback: ....

....
[2]

15

Section 5: Algorithms

Test 18

There are **8 questions** in this test. Give yourself **10 minutes** to answer them all.

1. What is the first step of the linear search algorithm?

   A Identify the middle item in the list.

   B Look at the first item in the list.

   C Split the list in half.

   [1]

2. Ignoring any information about a problem that isn't important is called...

   A ... decomposition.

   B ... abstraction.

   [1]

Questions 3 – 6 are on the following flowchart.

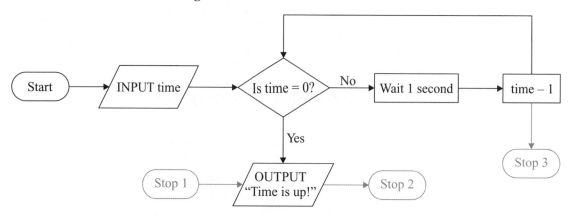

3. Which Stop box correctly completes the flowchart?

   A Stop 1

   B Stop 2

   C Stop 3

   [1]

4. The flowchart shows...

   A ... iteration only.

   B ... selection only.

   C ... selection and iteration.

   [1]

5. What does the flowchart represent?

   A A clock

   B A stopwatch

   C A countdown

   [1]

6. What command does the diamond box represent in the flowchart?

   A Decision

   B Sub Program

   C Process

   [1]

7. Put the following words into alphabetical order using the insertion sort algorithm.

Orange, Kiwi, Pear, Banana, Apple

....

....

....

....

....

[4]

8. Balthazar's Bookshop calculates an employee's monthly pay using the algorithm below.

```
input employeeName
input hoursWorked
totalPay = hoursWorked × 9
```

Outline what each line of the algorithm does.

....

....

....

[2]

If at least £10,000 of stock is sold in a month, employees now receive a £50 bonus. Complete the flowchart below to calculate and output an employee's new monthly pay. The sub program PAY represents the algorithm described above.

Start → | PAY |

Stop

[3]

15

Test 19

There are **9 questions** in this test. Give yourself **10 minutes** to answer them all.

1. Which of the following search algorithms can only be carried out on an ordered list?

   A Linear search

   B Binary search

   [1]

2. Computational thinking is used to…

   A … improve the efficiency of an existing program or piece of code.

   B … turn a problem into something a computer can help you solve.

   [1]

3. A programmer solves a complex task by writing many small sub programs. This is an example of…

   A … decomposition.

   B … abstraction.

   C … authentication.

   [1]

4. An online dictionary uses a program to sort a very large list of unordered words into alphabetical order. Which sorting algorithm would sort the list most efficiently?

   A Bubble sort

   B Insertion sort

   C Merge sort

   [1]

Questions 5 and 6 are on the following algorithms.

Algorithm 1
```
ask user to enter number of litres
input litres
pints = litres × 1.76
output pints
```

Algorithm 2
```
Take the number of litres and convert it
into pints and then output that answer
```

5. A benefit of using Algorithm 1 over Algorithm 2 is that…

   A … it can be more easily converted into a programming language.

   B … it can be interpreted by all programming languages.

   [1]

6. Each algorithm is written in pseudocode. An issue with Algorithm 2 is that…

   A … it does not use the proper syntax of a programming language.

   B … it is vague and unstructured.

   [1]

Section 5: Algorithms

7. Give two advantages of using an insertion sort.

1. ....

....

2. ....

....

[2]

8. Use a bubble sort to put the following numbers in ascending order,
while showing the order at the end of each pass: 7, 12, 14, 2, 8

....

....

....

....

....

....

[3]

9. A film streaming website uses an algorithm to restrict which films a user can view.
Draw a flowchart to show this algorithm. Your flowchart should:
- Have one input for the user's age and one input for the age rating of the film.
- Allow or deny access depending on whether the user is old enough to view the film.

[4]

15

Section 6: Programming

Test 20

There are **9 questions** in this test. Give yourself **10 minutes** to answer them all.

1. A procedure...

   A   ... always takes at least one parameter.

   B   ... never returns a value.

[1]

2. True or False? "Records can only contain values which are all of the same data type."

   A   True

   B   False

[1]

3. Which of the following data types could store the value 45.31?

   A   Integer

   B   Real

   C   Boolean

[1]

4. Which expression evaluates to `true`?

   A   `3 < 5 AND 1 > 2`

   B   `1 != 1 OR 4 < 5`

   C   `NOT(7 > 3)`

[1]

Questions 5 and 6 are on the following table and SQL statement.

Table: seatingPlan				
ID	firstName	lastName	dateOfBirth	seatNum
1	Humza	Ahmed	08/02/1993	4B
2	Janet	Swan	13/12/1986	13K
3	Ollie	Fisher	29/05/1996	24A
4	Agata	Kowalski	10/03/1990	7D

```
SELECT firstName, dateOfBirth FROM seatingPlan WHERE seatNum = 24A
```

5. What will the SQL statement above return?

   A

Humza	08/02/1993

   B

Fisher	29/05/1996

   C

Ollie	29/05/1996

[1]

6. Which SQL statement would return all records in the table?

   A   `SELECT ID FROM seatingPlan`

   B   `SELECT * FROM seatNum`

   C   `SELECT * FROM seatingPlan`

[1]

7. What is meant by casting?

....

[1]

8. The *n*th square number can be found by adding up the first *n* odd numbers.
Complete the algorithm below to write the first 10 square numbers
to a text file called 'output.txt' and close the file.

```
01  nums = open(................................................................)

02  sqNum = 0

03  for n = 1 to 19 step ........................

04      sqNum = sqNum + n

05      ........................................................................

06  next n

07  ........................................................................
```

[4]

9. The array scoresArch holds the
scores of five archers in a competition.
scoresArch[1, 2] contains the value 8.

Write a line of code to insert a score
of 7 into the empty element in the array.

		Archer				
		0	**1**	**2**	**3**	**4**
Shot	**0**	5	3	10	6	8
	1	3	1	8	7	7
	2	4	1	9	10	

....

[1]

Write a function that takes the array and an archer number
as parameters and returns an archer's total score.

[3]

15

Test 21

There are **11 questions** in this test. Give yourself **10 minutes** to answer them all.

1. What will 23 DIV 4 return?

    A 6

    B 3

    C 5

    [1]

2. True or False? "The value of a constant can't be modified whilst a program is running."

    A True

    B False

    [1]

Questions 3 and 4 are on the following array.

```
01  array goals [2, 2]
02  goals[0, 0] = 5
03  goals[0, 1] = 11
04  goals[1, 0] = 4
05  goals[1, 1] = 7
```

3. goals is an example of a...

    A 1D array with 4 elements

    B 2D array with 4 elements

    C 2D array with 2 elements

    [1]

4. Why is it appropriate to store this data in an array?

    A No data uses the string data type.

    B All the data is of the same data type.

    [1]

5. Which logic gate gives an output of 1 if either input is 1?

    A AND gate

    B NOT gate

    C OR gate

    [1]

6. Parameters are…

    A … types of variable used to pass information into a sub program.

    B … the actual information that is passed into a sub program.

    [1]

7. What does ASC(c) do?

    A Returns the ASCII code for the character "c".

    B Returns true if "c" is in the ASCII character set.

    [1]

8. A program deploys the rear wing of a supercar when the variable speed is greater than 70. Which of the following would be the most appropriate in this program?

    A An IF statement.

    B A SWITCH statement.

    [1]

9. A user registers on a website with the details on the right.

    State the output of the following lines of code:

    ```
    firstName = "John"
    lastName = "Jones"
    age = "34"
    ```

    `print(age.length)` ....

    `print("Mr. " + lastName.upper)` ....

    [2]

    Write program code to print a random character from `firstName`.

    [2]

10. Give one benefit of an IF-ELSEIF statement over a SWITCH statement.

    ....

    ....

    [1]

11. The table `flightPaths` below shows information about flights from UK airports.

flightNumber	depAirport	destAirport	depTime
AA442	Manchester	New York	09:45
A7757	Liverpool	Las Vegas	11:33
F142	Liverpool	Menorca	08:30
KL114	Heathrow	Edinburgh	16:42

    Write an SQL statement to return:

    the flight number and destination of all flights departing from Liverpool

    ....

    ....

    [1]

    the departure airport and departure time for flight F142

    ....

    ....

    [1]

    15

44

There are **9 questions** in this test. Give yourself **10 minutes** to answer them all.

1. Which logic gate gives an output of 0 if both inputs are 0?

   A   AND gate

   B   OR gate

   C   Both AND and OR gates

   [1]

2. Given that x = "CompSci" and test = x.subString(4,1), what is the output of print(test)?

   A   S

   B   p

   C   Comp

   [1]

Questions 3 to 6 are on the following program.

```
highScore = 89
playerScore = input("Please enter your score")
if playerScore < 1 OR playerScore > 100 then
    print("Invalid score entered")
elseif playerScore > highScore then
    print("New high score, well done!")
elseif playerScore < highScore then
    print("You did not beat the high score")
else
    print("You equalled the high score!")
endif
```

3. The highScore variable has an integer data type. Using the correct data type makes code...

   A   ... less memory efficient.

   B   ... more robust.

   [1]

4. The flow of the program is controlled using...

   A   ... a selection statement.

   B   ... an iteration statement.

   C   ... both selection and iteration statements.

   [1]

5. Which of these inputs would result in the output Invalid score entered?

   A   1

   B   1.1

   C   101

   [1]

6. What would the program output if the input was 90?

   A   You equalled the high score!

   B   New high score, well done!

   C   You did not beat the high score

   [1]

7. Explain the difference between the $=$ operator and the $==$ operator.

....

....

[2]

8. Why is it suitable to use the string data type to store a postcode?

....

....

[1]

9. Mike has written three procedures:
A. `listUsers()`   B. `createUser()`   C. `deleteUser()`

Write program code using a SWITCH statement which:
- asks a user to input a letter and runs the matching procedure,
  e.g. an input of "B" runs the `createUser` procedure.
- displays a message if an input has no matching procedure.

[4]

Mike defines a local variable in the `listUsers` procedure.
He later tries to reuse the variable outside of the procedure. Explain what will happen.

....

....

[2]

15

Test 23

There are **9 questions** in this test. Give yourself **10 minutes** to answer them all.

1. Which operator is used to raise a number to a power?

   A DIV

   B ^

   C MOD

   [1]

2. Which of the following numbers could be generated using `random(1, 10)`?

   A 10

   B 5.0

   C 15

   [1]

Questions 3 to 6 are on the following program.

```
01 warningSiren = false
02 temp = input()  //temp is the initial temperature of the reactor.
03 rads = input()  //rads is the initial radiation of the reactor.
04 if rads < 0.3 then
05    while temp < 300
06       print("Temperature is at " + str(temp) + " degrees.")
07       runReactor()  //Activates reactor. Increases value of temp.
08    endwhile
09 endif
10 warningSiren = true //Plays warning siren in facility.
11 print("Evacuate the facility now!")
```

3. Why is casting needed in line 06?

   A There are more than two strings being concatenated.

   B temp has a real data type but needs to be concatenated with a string.

   [1]

4. When does the WHILE loop check the value of `temp`?

   A During the loop.

   B At the end of the loop.

   C At the start of the loop.

   [1]

5. Which of the following statements is true?

   A The values of rads and temp determine whether a warning siren plays.

   B The value of warningSiren determines if a message is printed.

   [1]

6. If 0.3 is the initial radiation and 90 is the initial temperature, what is the first string that would be output by the program?

   A Temperature is at 90 degrees.

   B Evacuate the facility now!

   [1]

7. Complete the following truth table.

A	B	C	A AND B	NOT C	X = (A AND B) OR (NOT C)
0	0	0		1	
0	0	1		0	
0	1	0		1	
0	1	1		0	
1	0	0		1	
1	0	1		0	
1	1	0		1	
1	1	1		0	

[2]

8. The words below are stored in an array called `pets`.

rex	summer	fudge	mickey	rebel

Complete the algorithm to change the contents of the array to all uppercase.

```
01  i = 0

02  do

03      pets[i] = ...........................................................

04      i = i + 1

05  until i == ....................................
```

[2]

Explain the effect of deleting line 04.

....

....

[2]

9. Write a function called `average` which takes three integer parameters and returns
    their average (mean). Only the whole number part of the average should be returned.

[3]

15

Section 6: Programming

Section 7: Design, Testing and IDEs

Test 24

There are **12 questions** in this test. Give yourself **10 minutes** to answer them all.

1. A program only allows users to input an integer between 0 and 10. This is an example of...

   A ... input diagnostics.

   B ... input validation.

   [1]

2. A good test plan should...

   A ... outline what will be tested and how it will be tested.

   B ... only test for one potential way a user may misuse a program.

   [1]

3. A program requires the user to enter their age in whole years. Which of the following test data for the program is not erroneous?

   A 4£

   B 64

   C −28.0

   [1]

4. Which of these is not a part of defensive design?

   A Anticipating how a program may be used incorrectly in the future.

   B Authenticating users of a program to prevent unauthorised access.

   C Encrypting a program so it cannot be deciphered.

   [1]

5. Which of these translators will stop when they reach the first error in a program?

   A Compiler

   B Interpreter

   [1]

6. Iterative testing takes place...

   A ... during development.

   B ... after development is complete.

   [1]

7. Structure diagrams break a program down into modules. What is an advantage of this?

   A Multiple programmers can work on the same module at the same time.

   B A module can be fixed without affecting the rest of the program.

   C The program will contain fewer errors.

   [1]

8. Which of these is a valid way of reducing the number of characters in a program without compromising its functionality?

   A Removing all indentation.

   B Renaming all variables as single letters ("a", "b", "c" etc.)

   C Replacing repeated code with functions or procedures.

   [1]

9. What is a logic error?

....

....

[1]

10. Describe a feature of an IDE which can be used to identify logic errors.

....

....

[1]

11. The formula for triangle number n is $0.5\,n(n+1)$. The procedure on the right takes a parameter n and prints the first n triangle numbers.

```
01 procedure triNumbers(n)
02    for i = 1 to n
03       triangle = 0.5 * i * (i + 1)
04       print(triangle)
05    next i
06 endprocedure
```

Complete the trace table below when `triNumbers(4)` is called.

n	i	triangle
		1
	2	
		6

[3]

12. Why is it important to keep code well-maintained?

....

....

....

....

[2]

15

Section 7: Design, Testing and IDEs

Test 25

There are **10 questions** in this test. Give yourself **10 minutes** to answer them all.

1. True or False? "Trace tables can help identify any logic errors within code."

   A True

   B False

   [1]

2. A compiler...

   A ... translates and runs the source code one instruction at a time.

   B ... translates all of the source code and creates an executable file.

   [1]

3. Final (terminal) testing is used...

   A ... to test that each individual module of a program works correctly in isolation.

   B ... to test for errors in the main program when modules interact with each other.

   [1]

4. Which part of an IDE may include automatic features to format comments?

   A Run-time environment

   B Breakpoints

   C Code editor

   [1]

5. Which of the following statements about modules is correct?

   A A module is a smaller part of a larger program.

   B A module cannot be reused to write a program in the future.

   [1]

6. Error diagnostic tools...

   A ... can identify syntax errors in code and give the location of the errors.

   B ... auto-correct any logic errors in code and give the location of the errors.

   [1]

7. Asking a user to enter a username and password is a type of…

   A ... validation.

   B ... encryption.

   C ... authentication.

   [1]

8. A software company is developing a program for an embedded system with limited memory. Which type of language would be most appropriate to write in?

   A High-level language

   B Low-level language

   [1]

Section 7: Design, Testing and IDEs

9. Kaira needs to create an email address. Give two input validation checks that may be used to check her email address is in an acceptable format.

1. ....

2. ....

[2]

10. The program below takes an input and returns a student's grade.

```
01  number = input("Please enter your mark")
02  total = 80
03  percentage = number/total * 100
04  if (percentage >= 70 AND percentage <= 100) then
05  print("You have achieved a grade A")
06  elseif (percentage >= 50 AND percentage < 70) then
07  print("You have achieved a grade B")
08  elseif (percentage >= 30 AND percentage < 50) then
09  print("You have achieved a grade C")
10  else
11  print("You have failed")
12  endif
```

Give two ways, using examples from the code, of how the maintainability of the program could be improved.

1. ....

2. ....

[2]

The program does not work when erroneous data is input.
Complete the test plan below to test for other potential issues of the program.

Type of data	Test data	Reason for testing	Actual Outcome
	40		"You have achieved a grade C"
	90	To ensure the program can handle inputs of the correct data type that should be rejected	
Boundary	80		

[3]

15

Section 7: Design, Testing and IDEs

Test 26

There are **11 questions** in this test. Give yourself **10 minutes** to answer them all.

1. What information should be given about each field when creating a record structure?

   A Data type and field name

   B Data type and field length

   C Data arguments and field length

   [1]

2. True or False? "`random(0, 10)` generates a random integer between 1 and 9."

   A True

   B False

   [1]

3. Combining two string variables is called...

   A ... concentration.

   B ... coordination.

   C ... concatenation.

   [1]

4. A DO UNTIL loop is controlled by a condition...

   A ... at the start of the loop.

   B ... at the end of the loop.

   [1]

5. A binary search is performed on a list of 5 items. What is the greatest number of comparisons needed to find an item?

   A 2

   B 3

   C 4

   [1]

6. When testing a program, boundary data should be used to...

   A ... test that the program correctly processes inputs at the limit of what it should be able to handle.

   B ... test that the program can handle invalid inputs.

   [1]

7. Developing a logical set of instructions to solve a particular problem is known as...

   A ... abstraction.

   B ... decomposition.

   C ... algorithmic thinking.

   [1]

8. Which of the following statements is false?

   A A function can have more than one parameter.

   B A function never returns a value.

   C A function is a type of sub program.

   [1]

9. Which set of input values will give an output of 1 in the logic circuit below?

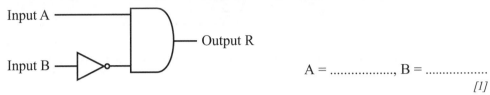

Input A ——
Input B ——

Output R

A = ..., B = ...

[1]

Write the logic statement for the logic circuit.

R = ...

[1]

10. All guests of a hotel must rate their stay on a scale from 1 to 5 when checking out. Complete the flowchart below to:

• ask a guest to enter their name and a rating (1, 2, 3, 4 or 5).
• output a message that thanks the guest with their name if a valid input is entered.
• output an appropriate message if an invalid input is entered.

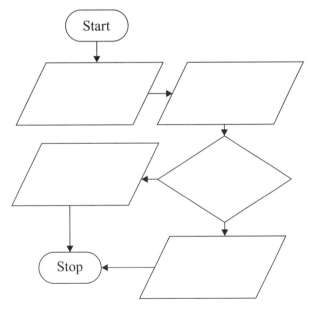

[3]

11. Explain how global variables can sometimes cause problems in large programs and why local variables are often preferred by developers.

....

....

....

[2]

15

Test 27

There are **9 questions** in this test. Give yourself **10 minutes** to answer them all.

1. A sub program flowchart box is used...

   A ... to show the start of an iteration.

   B ... at the start of a decision.

   C ... to reference another flowchart.

   [1]

2. Which of the following is an example of a logic error?

   A A `DIV` operator is used instead of a `MOD` operator.

   B A function is called but a bracket is missing.

   [1]

Questions 3 to 6 are on the following table and SQL statement.

Table: boats				
make	model	engineType	radarFitted	engineSize
Swift	Racer	Petrol	False	2.5
June	Spirit	Petrol	False	1.4
Swift	Ranger	Diesel	True	2.0
Ocean Crawler	Enterprise	Diesel	True	1.6

```
SELECT _____ FROM boats WHERE engineSize < 1.6
```

3. Which of these statements is correct?

   A Each row of the table is an array.

   B Each row of the table is a record.

   [1]

4. What field name is missing from the SQL statement above if 'Spirit' is returned?

   A `engineSize`

   B `model`

   C `engineType`

   [1]

5. Which data type is most appropriate for the field `radarFitted`?

   A String

   B Character

   C Boolean

   [1]

6. What is an appropriate validation check to use on the field `engineSize`?

   A Check all data is greater than 0.

   B Check all data is "True" or "False".

   C Check all data is less than 2.0.

   [1]

Mixed Tests for Paper 2

7. The function on the right takes num as a parameter. Complete the first four rows of the trace table below when mystery(10) is called.

```
function mystery(num)
    count = 0
    for i = 1 to num
        if num MOD i == 0
            count = count + 1
        endif
    next i
    return count
endfunction
```

num	i	num MOD i	count
10	–	–	0

[3]

What is the purpose of the function mystery()?

....

....

[1]

8. A merge sort is being carried out on the following letters: Z C G A L B T F
The algorithm has already split the list so that each letter is in its own list.
Complete the algorithm to put the letters in alphabetical order.

[3]

9. Give two benefits of a programmer using a high-level language rather than a low-level language.

1. ....

....

2. ....

....

[2]

15

Test 28

There are **11 questions** in this test. Give yourself **10 minutes** to answer them all.

1. Which of the following
    statements evaluates to 2?

    A   `11 MOD 3`

    B   `10/3`

    C   `3 DIV 2`

    [1]

2. Which type of flowchart box is
    a rectangle with rounded corners?

    A   Sub Program

    B   Start/Stop

    C   Decision

    [1]

3. What would the logic statement
    `33 > 10 OR 5 < 3` evaluate to?

    A   TRUE

    B   FALSE

    [1]

4. What would be the output of
    `firstname.left(i)`?

    A   The first `i` characters of `firstname`.

    B   The final `i` characters of `firstname`.

    C   The string `firstname`, excluding
          the character in position `i`.

    [1]

5. Which of the following can improve the
    maintainability of a program?

    A   Using multiple forms of authentication.

    B   Using sub programs.

    C   Removing all comments.

    [1]

6. How many possible combinations of inputs
    are there for a logic circuit with 3 inputs?

    A   8

    B   10

    C   9

    [1]

7. Which of these would not make a password-
    based authentication system more secure?

    A   Enforce users to change their
          password every month.

    B   Enforce users to use no numbers
          or symbols in a password.

    [1]

8. Which of the following
    is a type of data structure?

    A   A trace table

    B   A procedure

    C   A record

    [1]

9. Rajesh has written the procedure below to simulate 10 rolls of a 20-sided dice.

```
01  procedure diceRoll()
02      for n = 1 to 10
03          roll = random(1.0 to 20.0)
04      next n
05      print(roll)
06  endprocedure
```

There are two errors in his code.
Suggest how you would refine his procedure so that it works as intended.

....

....

[2]

10. Describe two features of an IDE that can make writing a program easier.

1. ....

....

2. ....

....

[2]

11. The sales array holds the sales of a shop for each day of the week.
For example, sales[0] holds the sales for Monday.

Complete the rollingSales function below that takes an integer parameter, num,
and returns the total sales for that many days, starting from Monday.
For example, rollingSales(2) should return the total sales for Monday and Tuesday.

```
function rollingSales(num)




endfunction
```

[3]

15

Test 29

There are **8 questions** in this test. Give yourself **10 minutes** to answer them all.

1. A program that compiles successfully but does something unexpected when it is running contains...

   A   ... syntax errors.

   B   ... logic errors.

[1]

2. Which logic gate only takes a single input?

   A   NOT

   B   AND

   C   OR

[1]

3. Which of these commands is required first when reading data from a text file?

   A   `readLine()`

   B   `open()`

   C   `dataRead()`

[1]

4. Which of these lines of code does not use a comparison operator?

   A   `x = 9 * 8`

   B   `y == 10`

   C   `z > 7`

[1]

Questions 5 and 6 are on the following flowchart.

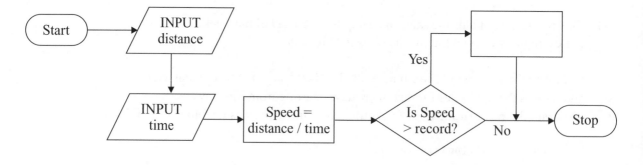

5. Which programming construct is used at the diamond box?

   A   Selection

   B   Sequence

   C   Iteration

[1]

6. Which of these commands should be used in the empty box to update `Record`?

   A   `Record = Speed`

   B   `Speed = Record`

   C   `Record = Record + Speed`

[1]

7. Sophia wants to develop a recipe app for her smartphone. The app will ask a user to input ingredients and will return a list of recipes that can be made. Part of a structure diagram for the app is shown below.

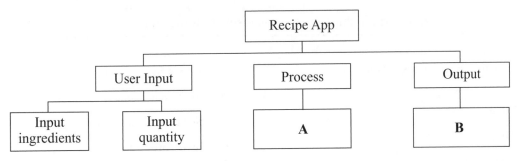

Suggest a module or task that would be appropriate for Box A and Box B.

Box A: ....

Box B: ....

[2]

Which technique of computational thinking is shown with a structure diagram?

....

[1]

8. The text file 'mass.txt' on the right shows the masses of five objects. A scientist wants to write a program to analyse these values.

Write program code that reads each value from 'mass.txt' and puts them into a different element of an array called `data`.
Your program must contain:

- a WHILE loop.
- the endOfFile() command.

mass.txt

332.1
461.4
74.1
24.6
100.0

[6]   **15**

Test 30

There are **11 questions** in this test. Give yourself **10 minutes** to answer them all.

1. Which is the most suitable data type to store the value 1.7?

    A   Integer

    B   Real

    C   Character

    [1]

2. What does SQL stand for?

    A   Systematic Query Library

    B   Scripted Query Look-Up

    C   Structured Query Language

    [1]

3. True or False? "Defensive design involves anticipating how a user may misuse a program."

    A   True

    B   False

    [1]

4. Given that `cityName = "Liverpool"`, which of these would output `"erp"`?

    A   `cityName.subString(3,3)`

    B   `cityName.String(3,5)`

    C   `cityName.subString(4,3)`

    [1]

5. An algorithm written in pseudocode...

    A   ... should always use the proper syntax of a programming language.

    B   ... can show the same solution to a problem that a flowchart can.

    [1]

6. What are breakpoints used for in an IDE?

    A   To show lines of code that don't have any comments.

    B   To provide syntax highlighting.

    C   To pause the program on specific lines to allow for further investigation.

    [1]

7. Which of the following statements would evaluate to TRUE when a = 49?

    A   `a > 49 AND a < 49`

    B   `a >= 50 OR a <= 75`

    C   `a != 49`

    [1]

8. A list has 4 items. What is the maximum number of comparisons needed to sort the list using an insertion sort?

    A   4

    B   6

    C   8

    [1]

---

9. Complete the truth table below.

A	B	A AND B	NOT (A AND B)
False	False		
False	True		
True	False		
True	True		

[2]

10. The program below counts the number of prizes left in a competition.

```
01  beachprize = 100
02  skiprize = 50
03  code = input("Enter a code for a chance to win!")
04  switch type:
05     case "Beach108":
06         beachprize = beachprize - 1
07         print("You have won a beach prize!")
08     case "Ski209":
09         skiprize = skiprize - 1
10         print("You have won a ski prize!"
11     case default:
12         print("You have not won this time!")
```

Identify three errors in this program.

1. ....

2. ....

3. ....

[3]

11. The start of a function for a search algorithm is shown below.

```
function searchAlgorithm(fArray, fItem)
    startArray = 0
    endArray = len(fArray) - 1 //len returns the size of an array.
    while startArray != endArray
        midArray = (startArray + endArray) DIV 2
...
```

Identify the algorithm the function represents. Give a reason for your answer.

....

....

[2]

15

Answers

Section 1: Components of a Computer System

Test 1 — Pages 2–3

1. C *[1 mark]*   2. A *[1 mark]*
3. B *[1 mark]*   4. C *[1 mark]*
5. A *[1 mark]*   6. A *[1 mark]*
7. A *[1 mark]*   8. B *[1 mark]*
9. E.g. dishwasher / microwave / TV / washing machine *[1 mark]*
10. It can make a computer slow to respond when switching between applications or performing memory-intensive tasks *[1 mark]*.
11. E.g. Encryption software scrambles data so it can't be read *[1 mark]*. The intended reader can decrypt the data with the correct 'key' *[1 mark]*.
12. E.g. The Control Unit sends signals to load the address of the program counter into the MAR *[1 mark]*. The data/instruction in that memory address is then fetched from memory and stored in the MDR *[1 mark]*. The PC is incremented to point to the address of the next instruction *[1 mark]*.

Test 2 — Pages 4–5

1. B *[1 mark]*   2. B *[1 mark]*
3. B *[1 mark]*   4. B *[1 mark]*
5. C *[1 mark]*   6. C *[1 mark]*
7. A *[1 mark]*   8. C *[1 mark]*
9. To process data and instructions to make a computer system function correctly *[1 mark]*.
10. Any two from: e.g. Provide a user interface. / Handle file and disk management. / Manage user accounts and security. / Control the CPU and memory resources. *[2 marks]*
11. Any two advantages: e.g. The SSD will not require defragmenting. / The SSD will withstand shocks better than the HDD. / The SSD is silent. *[2 marks]*

    Any two disadvantages: e.g. The SSD is likely to cost more than the HDD. / The SSD is likely to have a lower capacity than the HDD. / The SSD has a shorter read/write life and will deteriorate over time. *[2 marks]*

Test 3 — Pages 6–7

1. B *[1 mark]*   2. A *[1 mark]*
3. A *[1 mark]*   4. C *[1 mark]*
5. A *[1 mark]*   6. B *[1 mark]*
7. C *[1 mark]*   8. C *[1 mark]*
9. Compressing the file will reduce the size of the file, so it will take up less storage space / will be quicker to transfer over the Internet *[1 mark]*.
10. The accumulator stores intermediate results of calculations performed by the ALU *[1 mark]*.
11. Any two from: e.g. Password / PIN / User-access levels / Fingerprint scanner / Retina scanner *[2 marks]*
12. E.g. USB Flash Drive *[1 mark]*

    Any two from: e.g. USB flash drives offer appropriate storage capacity for the files. / They are small and portable. / They are robust and unlikely to get damaged. / Most laptops have USB ports, so it is appropriate for students. *[2 marks]*

Section 2: Data Representation

Test 4 — Pages 8–9

1. C *[1 mark]*   2. C *[1 mark]*
3. A *[1 mark]*   4. B *[1 mark]*
5. A *[1 mark]*   6. A *[1 mark]*
7. B *[1 mark]*   8. A *[1 mark]*
9.
$$\begin{array}{r} 0\,1\,0\,1\,0\,1\,0\,1 \\ +\ 0\,1\,1\,0\,1\,1\,0\,1 \\ \hline 1\,1\,0\,0\,0\,0\,1\,0 \\ \hline \end{array}$$

    [1 mark for working, 1 mark for correct answer]
10. Overflow is when a calculation *[1 mark]* produces an answer that has more bits than the CPU was expecting *[1 mark]*.
11. Lossless compression *[1 mark]*.

    Data is temporarily removed from the image, which is then restored when the image is opened *[1 mark]*. Therefore, the photographer can recover the original high-quality image as no data is lost *[1 mark]*.

Test 5 — Pages 10–11

1. A *[1 mark]*   2. A *[1 mark]*
3. A *[1 mark]*   4. A *[1 mark]*
5. C *[1 mark]*   6. C *[1 mark]*

7. B *[1 mark]*   8. A *[1 mark]*
9. z is the next character after y, so it is one binary value greater: 01111010 *[1 mark]*

    File size = no. of bits per character × no. of characters *[1 mark]* = 8 × 30 = 240 bits *[1 mark]*
10. 5 = 5 in denary and 0101 in binary. E = 14 in denary and 1110 in binary. Put the nibbles together to get 01011110 *[1 mark for working, 1 mark for correct answer]*
11. E.g. Benefit: the digital recording will be of higher quality / closer to the original vocals *[1 mark]*. Drawback: the size of the audio file will increase *[1 mark]*.

Test 6 — Pages 12–13

1. B *[1 mark]*   2. C *[1 mark]*
3. B *[1 mark]*   4. A *[1 mark]*
5. B *[1 mark]*   6. A *[1 mark]*
7. C *[1 mark]*   8. A *[1 mark]*
9. 00000011 *[1 mark]* 00001101 *[1 mark]*

    shiftR(11011001) returns an answer where the '1001' bits have been lost, so the fractional part of the division would not be included *[1 mark]*.
10. E.g. Compression makes the file smaller in size *[1 mark]*, so it will be faster to upload and send via email *[1 mark]*.
11. The new binary number is 10010001, which is 128 + 16 + 1 = 145 as a denary number *[1 mark for working, 1 mark for correct answer]*.

Section 3: Networks

Test 7 — Pages 14–15

1. A *[1 mark]*   2. A *[1 mark]*
3. B *[1 mark]*   4. C *[1 mark]*
5. A *[1 mark]*   6. A *[1 mark]*
7. C *[1 mark]*   8. B *[1 mark]*
9. Star topology *[1 mark]*
10. E.g. A weak password is easier to guess, so his account could be broken into via a brute force attack *[1 mark]*. The anti-malware software may not detect newer versions of malware attempting to be installed *[1 mark]*.

Answers

11. Any two advantages: e.g. Files can be accessed from any device with Internet access. / Security and backups are provided. / Saves space on hard drives, reducing the need to buy larger hard drives. *[2 marks]*

Any two disadvantages: e.g. Files cannot be accessed without an Internet connection. / Reliant on the cloud host to ensure data is secure. / Subscription fees can be expensive in the long term. *[2 marks]*

Test 8 — Pages 16–17
1. C *[1 mark]*
2. B *[1 mark]*
3. A *[1 mark]*
4. B *[1 mark]*
5. B *[1 mark]*
6. C *[1 mark]*
7. A *[1 mark]*
8. B *[1 mark]*
9. E.g. Lock network hardware like servers in a secure room and only give keys to trusted people *[1 mark]*.
10. E.g. It is many characters in length *[1 mark]*. / It contains a mixture of letters and symbols etc. *[1 mark]*.
11. E.g. Company A has IT specialists which could install and update all employees' software at the same time in a client-server network *[1 mark]*. It will be easier to keep track of and backup files as they are stored centrally *[1 mark]*.

Company B has no IT specialists. A peer-to-peer network would be easy to set up and maintain *[1 mark]* and wouldn't require any expensive hardware or IT specialists *[1 mark]*.

Test 9 — Pages 18–19
1. B *[1 mark]*
2. A *[1 mark]*
3. B *[1 mark]*
4. C *[1 mark]*
5. C *[1 mark]*
6. A *[1 mark]*
7. B *[1 mark]*
8. C *[1 mark]*
9. HTTPS / HTTP Secure / Hyper Text Transfer Protocol Secure *[1 mark]*
10. Any two from: e.g. The cloud app can be accessed on any device. / Cloud apps are run on the cloud service provider's hardware, so you do not need a powerful computer to run memory-intensive apps. / The cloud service provider will keep the app up-to-date so you don't have to. *[2 marks]*

11. User access levels control which parts of a network that different groups of users can and cannot access *[1 mark]*.
12. Any three from: e.g. Files can be shared easily. / Devices such as printers can be shared across the business. / Devices can share an Internet connection. / Employees can log on to their accounts from any device on the network. *[3 marks]*

Test 10 — Pages 20–21
1. A *[1 mark]*
2. B *[1 mark]*
3. A *[1 mark]*
4. A *[1 mark]*
5. A *[1 mark]*
6. C *[1 mark]*
7. A *[1 mark]*
8. A *[1 mark]*
9. A DoS attack is where someone tries to stop users accessing part of a network or website by flooding a network with traffic *[1 mark]*.
10. Any two from: e.g. Pentest the network regularly. / Enforce user access levels to limit access to sensitive data. / Use firewalls. / Encrypt all sensitive data. *[2 marks]*
11. E.g. IPv4 addresses use 32 bits whereas IPv6 uses 128 bits *[1 mark]*. IPv4 addresses are given as four denary numbers whereas IPv6 are given as eight hex numbers *[1 mark]*.
12. Any two from: e.g. Number of devices connected to the network. / High-bandwidth activities, such as streaming or online gaming. / Interference from obstacles, such as walls. / Interference from other nearby wireless networks. *[2 marks]*

Section 4: Issues

Test 11 — Pages 22–23
1. B *[1 mark]*
2. B *[1 mark]*
3. B *[1 mark]*
4. A *[1 mark]*
5. B *[1 mark]*
6. C *[1 mark]*
7. B *[1 mark]*
8. A *[1 mark]*
9. E.g. Users of the cloud have to trust the company storing their data to protect it against loss or hackers. / Users may not fully understand how the company uses their data if they have not read the privacy agreement. *[1 mark]*

10. Cyberbullying is when somebody uses social media to deliberately harm somebody else *[1 mark]*.
11. E.g. Manufacturing requires large amounts of energy, which creates pollution *[1 mark]*. Large amounts of raw materials are used *[1 mark]*.
12. E.g. The Data Protection Act gives certain rights to customers which aren't being considered by the supermarket *[1 mark]*. E.g. the data is not being used for its specified purpose *[1 mark]*, and is being used in an unlawful way *[1 mark]*.

Test 12 — Pages 24–25
1. A *[1 mark]*
2. A *[1 mark]*
3. B *[1 mark]*
4. B *[1 mark]*
5. A *[1 mark]*
6. A *[1 mark]*
7. A *[1 mark]*
8. C *[1 mark]*
9. Computer surveillance is when someone monitors what people are doing on their computers *[1 mark]*.
10. He is likely to live in an area with poor reception quality and broadband speed *[1 mark]*. He may not be able to afford new technology with his low income *[1 mark]*.

The digital divide *[1 mark]*.
11. E.g. Teenagers can experience cyberbullying or trolling on social media sites *[1 mark]*. / Teenagers may come across inappropriate material or be at risk of exploitation on the Internet *[1 mark]*. / Teenagers are pressured into always having the latest device by their peers *[1 mark]*.

Mixed Tests for Paper 1
Test 13 — Pages 26–27
1. B *[1 mark]*
2. A *[1 mark]*
3. C *[1 mark]*
4. C *[1 mark]*
5. A *[1 mark]*
6. A *[1 mark]*
7. B *[1 mark]*
8. B *[1 mark]*
9. The size of the image file will increase *[1 mark]*.
10. Any two from: e.g. If a device fails or is disconnected, the rest of the network is unaffected. / It is easy to add new devices to the network. / Data goes straight to the central device, reducing the chance for data collisions. *[2 marks]*

Answers

11. E.g. Fewer physical servers are needed, so fewer natural resources are used to build them *[1 mark]* and less energy is needed to keep them running *[1 mark]*.

12. Gaps on a hard disk appear when files are moved, deleted or change size *[1 mark]*. New files are saved in different gaps *[1 mark]*.

Test 14 — Pages 28–29

1. B *[1 mark]*
2. A *[1 mark]*
3. C *[1 mark]*
4. C *[1 mark]*
5. A *[1 mark]*
6. A *[1 mark]*
7. A *[1 mark]*
8. C *[1 mark]*
9. E.g. Fewer waiters may be needed, so some could lose their jobs *[1 mark]*.
10. The OS manages memory resources so that applications do not interfere with each other *[1 mark]*. The OS divides CPU time between open applications, prioritising certain processes, so that instructions are executed efficiently *[1 mark]*.
11. E.g. 142 ÷ 16 = 8 r 14 *[1 mark]* 14 is E in hexadecimal, so 142 is 8E in hexadecimal *[1 mark]*
12. She would have higher capacity/ speed in primary storage *[1 mark]*, so the CPU could have quicker access to more data *[1 mark]*.

Test 15 — Pages 30–31

1. B *[1 mark]*
2. C *[1 mark]*
3. C *[1 mark]*
4. B *[1 mark]*
5. B *[1 mark]*
6. A *[1 mark]*
7. B *[1 mark]*
8. A *[1 mark]*
9. A WAP allows devices to connect wirelessly to a LAN *[1 mark]*.
10. Split into nibbles: 1010, 1110. 1010 = A and 1110 = E *[1 mark]* So 10101110 is AE in hex *[1 mark]*
11. Any two from: Gaining unauthorised access to a private network or device through hacking. / Accessing a network or device in order to commit a crime. / Purposefully spreading malware. *[2 marks]*
12. Any two from: e.g. Make users choose strong passwords / Ask for a random selection of characters / Lock accounts after a number of incorrect log-in attempts *[2 marks]*

Test 16 — Pages 32–33

1. C *[1 mark]*
2. B *[1 mark]*
3. C *[1 mark]*
4. A *[1 mark]*
5. C *[1 mark]*
6. C *[1 mark]*
7. B *[1 mark]*
8. A *[1 mark]*
9. 11001000 *[1 mark]*
10.

Primary Storage	Secondary Storage
RAM	Magnetic Hard Disk
ROM	SSD
Cache	Magnetic Tape

[2 marks for all correct, 1 mark for any four answers sorted correctly]

11. Positives: e.g. Open source software is often free, reducing development cost *[1 mark]*. / It can be modified to fit the company's needs *[1 mark]*.

Negatives: e.g. Open source software may not get regular updates, which leads to bugs etc. *[1 mark]*. / There is limited user documentation, making it harder to learn *[1 mark]*.

Test 17 — Pages 34–35

1. A *[1 mark]*
2. A *[1 mark]*
3. B *[1 mark]*
4. A *[1 mark]*
5. B *[1 mark]*
6. B *[1 mark]*
7. A *[1 mark]*
8. B *[1 mark]*
9. Secondary storage is non-volatile, so retains data without power *[1 mark]*.
10. (4 × 16) = 64 and F = 15, *[1 mark]* so 4F = 64 + 15 = 79 *[1 mark]*
11. Any two from: e.g. Take regular breaks. / Sit with a correct posture. / Sit a reasonable distance from the screen. / Use suitable lighting / etc. *[2 marks]*
12. Benefit: e.g. Wired connections are usually faster than wireless *[1 mark]*. Drawback: e.g. More wiring is needed to add devices to the network *[1 mark]*.

Section 5: Algorithms

Test 18 — Pages 36–37

1. B *[1 mark]*
2. B *[1 mark]*
3. B *[1 mark]*
4. C *[1 mark]*
5. C *[1 mark]*
6. A *[1 mark]*
7. Orange, <u>Kiwi</u>, Pear, Banana, Apple
Kiwi, Orange, <u>Pear</u>, Banana, Apple
Kiwi, Orange, Pear, <u>Banana</u>, Apple
Banana, Kiwi, Orange, Pear, <u>Apple</u>
Apple, Banana, Kiwi, Orange, Pear
[1 mark for each row from rows 2-5]

8. Lines 1 takes an input and stores the result as *employeeName*. Line 2 takes an input and stores the result as *hoursWorked*. Line 3 multiplies the input from Line 2/*hoursWorked* by 9. *[1 mark for one correct line, 1 mark for all other correct lines]*

E.g.

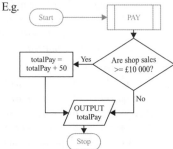

[1 mark for decision box with appropriate question, 1 mark for calculating new total pay, 1 mark for output]

Test 19 — Pages 38–39

1. B *[1 mark]*
2. B *[1 mark]*
3. A *[1 mark]*
4. C *[1 mark]*
5. A *[1 mark]*
6. B *[1 mark]*
7. Any two from: e.g. They can handle small lists very efficiently. / They are very memory efficient as all sorting is done in the original list. / They can quickly check if a list is already sorted. *[2 marks]*
8. First pass: 7, 12, 2, 8, 14 *[1 mark]* Second pass: 7, 2, 8, 12, 14 *[1 mark]* Third pass: 2, 7, 8, 12, 14 *[1 mark]* Fourth pass: no swaps, list is ordered.
9. E.g.

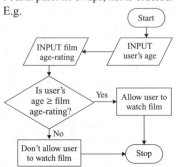

[1 mark for start and stop, 1 mark for input boxes, 1 mark for decision box with appropriate question, 1 mark for process boxes]

Answers

Section 6: Programming

Test 20 — Pages 40–41

1. B *[1 mark]*   2. B *[1 mark]*
3. B *[1 mark]*   4. B *[1 mark]*
5. C *[1 mark]*   6. C *[1 mark]*
7. Casting converts one data type to a different data type *[1 mark]*.
8. 01   *nums = open("output.txt")*
   03   *for n = 1 to 19 step 2*
   05   *nums.writeLine(sqNum)*
   07   *nums.close()*
   [1 mark for each correct line]
9. *scoresArch[2,4] = 7 [1 mark]*

   E.g.
   function totalScore(scores, arch)
      total = 0
      for i = 0 to 2
        total = total + scores[i, arch]
      next i
      return total
   endfunction
   [1 mark for defining a function with two parameters, 1 mark for calculating total, 1 mark for returning total]

Test 21 — Pages 42–43

1. C *[1 mark]*   2. A *[1 mark]*
3. B *[1 mark]*   4. B *[1 mark]*
5. C *[1 mark]*   6. A *[1 mark]*
7. A *[1 mark]*   8. A *[1 mark]*
9. 2 *[1 mark]*
   "Mr. JONES" *[1 mark]*

   E.g.
   x = random(0, 3)
   print(firstName.subString(x, 1))
   [1 mark for generating a random integer, 1 mark for correctly printing a random character]
10. E.g. An IF-ELSEIF statement can check multiple conditions at once, whereas a SWITCH statement can only check one variable *[1 mark]*.
11. *SELECT flightNumber, destAirport FROM flightPaths WHERE depAirport = "Liverpool" [1 mark]*

    SELECT depAirport, depTime FROM flightPaths WHERE flightNumber = "F142" [1 mark]

Test 22 — Pages 44–45

1. C *[1 mark]*   2. A *[1 mark]*
3. B *[1 mark]*   4. A *[1 mark]*
5. C *[1 mark]*   6. B *[1 mark]*
7. = assigns a value to a variable *[1 mark]*, whereas == compares values/variables and returns *true* if they match *[1 mark]*.
8. A postcode contains numbers and letters, which can be stored as a string *[1 mark]*.
9. E.g.
   userSelect = input("Input letter")
   switch userSelect:
     case "A":
      listUsers()
     case "B":
      createUser()
     case "C":
      deleteUser()
     default:
      print("Unrecognised selection")
   endswitch
   [1 mark for a user input, 1 mark for correct use of SWITCH, 1 mark for correct procedures, 1 mark for printing message for "default" case]

   He will get an error saying the variable is not defined *[1 mark]* because local variables can't be used outside of the procedure *[1 mark]*.

Test 23 — Pages 46–47

1. B *[1 mark]*   2. A *[1 mark]*
3. B *[1 mark]*   4. C *[1 mark]*
5. A *[1 mark]*   6. B *[1 mark]*
7.

A AND B	NOT C	X
0	1	1
0	0	0
0	1	1
0	0	0
0	1	1
0	0	0
1	1	1
1	0	1

[1 mark for each correct column]

8. 03   *pets[i] = pets[i].upper*
   05   *until i == 5*
   [1 mark for each correct line]

   As *i* would not increase, the DO UNTIL loop would run indefinitely *[1 mark]* and would only change "rex" to upper case *[1 mark]*.

9. E.g.
   function average(a, b, c)
      total = a + b + c
      ans = total DIV 3
      return ans
   endfunction
   [1 mark for defining a function with three parameters, 1 mark for finding the average, 1 mark for returning the whole number part]

Section 7: Design, Testing and IDEs

Test 24 — Pages 48–49

1. B *[1 mark]*   2. A *[1 mark]*
3. B *[1 mark]*   4. C *[1 mark]*
5. B *[1 mark]*   6. A *[1 mark]*
7. B *[1 mark]*   8. C *[1 mark]*
9. When a compiler/interpreter is able to run a program, but it doesn't behave as expected *[1 mark]*.
10. E.g. Breakpoints can be used to stop the program at specific points to allow a programmer to check things like the values of variables *[1 mark]*.
11.

n	i	triangle
4	1	1
4	2	3
4	3	6
4	4	10

[1 mark for each correct column]

12. E.g. to make it easy to read and modify *[1 mark]*. It also allows other programmers to understand what your program does *[1 mark]*.

Test 25 — Pages 50–51

1. A *[1 mark]*   2. B *[1 mark]*
3. B *[1 mark]*   4. C *[1 mark]*
5. A *[1 mark]*   6. A *[1 mark]*
7. C *[1 mark]*   8. B *[1 mark]*
9. E.g. Check it has an @ symbol and a .com or .co.uk *[1 mark]*. / Check it has fewer than a certain number of characters *[1 mark]*.
10. Any two from: e.g. Add comments to explain what the IF-ELSEIF statements do. / Use indentation inside the IF-ELSEIF statements. / Use the variable name "mark" instead of "number" for clarity. *[2 marks]*

Answers

First row
Type: Normal
Reason: To ensure the program can handle a correct input.
Second row
Type: Invalid
Outcome: "You have failed"
Third row
Reason: To ensure the program can handle the largest input value.
Outcome: "You have achieved a grade A"
[1 mark for each correct row]

Mixed Tests for Paper 2

Test 26 — Pages 52–53

1. A *[1 mark]*   2. B *[1 mark]*
3. C *[1 mark]*   4. B *[1 mark]*
5. B *[1 mark]*   6. A *[1 mark]*
7. C *[1 mark]*   8. B *[1 mark]*
9. A = 1, B = 0 *[1 mark]*
   R = A AND (NOT B) *[1 mark]*
10. E.g.

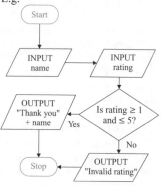

[1 mark for correct inputs, 1 mark for decision with branches labelled, 1 mark for correct outputs]

11. If a variable is global then you need to be careful that you don't change it or use the same name somewhere else in the program *[1 mark]*. Local variables can only be used inside a sub program, so developers can use them without risk of changing other parts of the main program *[1 mark]*.

Test 27 — Pages 54–55

1. C *[1 mark]*   2. A *[1 mark]*
3. B *[1 mark]*   4. B *[1 mark]*
5. C *[1 mark]*   6. A *[1 mark]*

7.

num	i	num MOD i	count
10	–	–	0
10	1	0	1
10	2	0	2
10	3	1	2

[1 mark for each correct row]

The function returns the number of factors of *num [1 mark]*.

8. Merge and order sub-lists until there is one list:
   CZ AG BL FT *[1 mark]*
   ACGZ BFLT *[1 mark]*
   ABCFGLTZ *[1 mark]*

9. Any two benefits: e.g. Easier for programmers to read and understand. / A single instruction of high-level code can represent many low-level instructions. / A programmer does not need to have knowledge about the internal structure of the CPU to write high-level code. / High-level code can work on multiple machines with different processors. *[2 marks]*

Test 28 — Pages 56–57

1. A *[1 mark]*   2. B *[1 mark]*
3. A *[1 mark]*   4. A *[1 mark]*
5. B *[1 mark]*   6. A *[1 mark]*
7. B *[1 mark]*   8. C *[1 mark]*
9. Replace line 03 with the code *roll = random(1, 20) [1 mark]*. Put the code on line 05 inside the loop, after line 03 *[1 mark]*.
10. E.g. A code editor can have auto-colour coding, auto-indent etc. to help readability. / A run-time environment can quickly run code within an IDE and show where any errors take place. *[2 marks]*
11. E.g.
    function rollingSales(num)
      total = 0
      for i = 1 to num
        total = total + sales[i - 1]
      next i
      return total
    endfunction
    [1 mark for correctly using the num parameter, 1 mark for using an appropriate loop to calculate total sales, 1 mark for returning total sales]

Test 29 — Pages 58–59

1. B *[1 mark]*   2. A *[1 mark]*
3. B *[1 mark]*   4. A *[1 mark]*
5. A *[1 mark]*   6. A *[1 mark]*
7. Box A: e.g. find recipes in database
   Box B: e.g. display recipes/costs
   [1 mark for each appropriate task]

   Decomposition *[1 mark]*.

8. E.g.
   array data[5]
   i = 0
   values = open("mass.txt")
   while NOT values.endOfFile()
     data[i] = values.readLine()
     i = i + 1
   endwhile
   values.close()
   [1 mark for creating an array, 1 mark for opening the file, 1 mark for a correct WHILE loop, 1 mark for use of endOfFile() to end the WHILE loop, 1 mark for assigning values to the array using readLine(), 1 mark for closing the file at the end]

Test 30 — Pages 60–61

1. B *[1 mark]*   2. C *[1 mark]*
3. A *[1 mark]*   4. A *[1 mark]*
5. B *[1 mark]*   6. C *[1 mark]*
7. B *[1 mark]*   8. B *[1 mark]*
9.

A AND B	NOT (A AND B)
False	True
False	True
False	True
True	False

[1 mark for each column]

10. Line 04: *switch type* should be *switch code [1 mark]*.
    Line 10: there is a missing closed bracket *[1 mark]*.
    There is no line of code to end the SWITCH statement *[1 mark]*.

11. The function represents a binary search *[1 mark]*, e.g. because line 5 identifies the middle item of the list/array *[1 mark]*.

COXP42